Mind-Boggling Lateral Thinking Puzzles
for Clued-up Kids

LAGOON
BOOKS

**Managing Editor:** Sarah Wells
**Editor:** Lucy Dear
**Contributors:** Fran Pickering, Philip Carter, Nick Daws,
Peter Sorrenti, Ann Marangos, Claire Redhead
**Cover, page design and layout:** Alan Shiner

Published by:
**Lagoon Books,
PO BOX 311, KT2 5QW, U.K.**

ISBN 1902813685

**© 2003 Lagoon Books, London**

Lagoon Books is a trade mark of
Lagoon Trading Company Limited.
All rights reserved.

Printed in Singapore

mind-boggling
LATERAL THINKING
puzzles

GREAT PUZZLES FOR CLUED-UP KIDS · GREAT PUZZLES FOR CLUED-UP KIDS

**GREAT PUZZLES FOR CLUED-UP KIDS!**

Other titles in the Mind-Boggling range include:

**MIND-BOGGLING
CODE BREAKER PUZZLES
(For Clued-up Kids)**

**MIND-BOGGLING
TRICKY LOGIC PUZZLES
(For Clued-up Kids)**

**MIND-BOGGLING
BRAIN TEASER PUZZLES
(For Clued-up Kids)**

# MIND BOGGLING
# LATERAL THINKING PUZZLES
# FOR CLUED-UP KIDS

Hey, kid! Think you're smart, do you?
Fancy yourself as a super-brain?
Then here's a challenge for you.

The fiendishly clever puzzles in this book have baffled
the brightest adult minds. Reckon you can do better?
Then here's a chance to strut your stuff and strike a
blow for kid power!

But be warned! Solving these puzzles isn't easy.
Simply being logical won't do it. Neither will knowing
loads of facts and figures from schoolbooks (yawn).

You'll need to be clever enough to see beyond the
obvious and imaginative enough to view problems in a
fresh light. Brave enough to take a leap into the
unknown, and return with some inspired deductions!

Think you can hack it? Then turn the page and
get started. The answers to all the puzzles are at
the back of the book. But you won't need them,
will you? Except to prove to everyone else that
you're right, of course!

# Shopping Bags

## Difficulty Rating ☆☆☆

Mrs Simpson was struggling through the mall
with three bags full of shopping.
She met her neighbor carrying four bags.
Who had the heavier load?

# Summer Holiday

## Difficulty Rating ⭐⭐

What always comes at the end of a summer holiday?

# Tea Time

### Difficulty Rating ☆☆☆☆

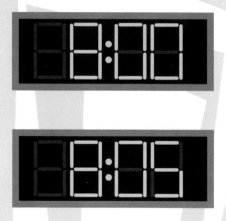

A man leaves home one night and drives over a mile to meet a friend for a cup of tea. When the man arrives home, the clock shows a time only five minutes later than when he left. How is this possible?

# Spoken Word

Difficulty Rating ☆

What is so delicate that if you say its name aloud,
you break it?

# Light Source

## Difficulty Rating ☆☆

A man lived all by himself. He never went out and no-one ever visited him. One day he watered all his plants, turned off all the lights and left the building, never to return again. His action resulted in six men getting wet. Why?

# Common Touch

### Difficulty Rating ✩✩✩

What do the cave, the boy and the river have in common?

# One Giant Leap

**Difficulty Rating** ☆☆

A woman steps to the edge of a very high building
and, while people look on,
she leaps off and falls several storeys.
The woman is not injured. Why?

# Bailing Out

### Difficulty Rating ★★★★

Flying over the Atlantic Ocean, a plane dumped
its cargo. Two boxes, one filled with tins of tea, the
other with feather pillows, were pushed from the cargo
hold at exactly the same time.
Which hit the ground first?

# Magic Circle

### Difficulty Rating ☆☆☆

EARTH   EARTH   EARTH   EARTH   EARTH

What does this have to do with a magic ring?

# Newspaper Round

Difficulty Rating ☆

Charlie brings the newspaper to Mr Hopkins every day,
even at the weekends. Charlie is never paid for this.
Why does he do this?

# Word Play

Difficulty Rating ☆☆☆

## Nothing is wrong with it;

## it is just odd or unusual.

## This is not commonly found in writing

What is unusual about this paragraph?

# Wrong Sign

Difficulty Rating ✮✮✮

**LIBRARY**

**IF YOU CAN'T**

**READ THE NOTICES,**

**ASK FOR HELP**

What is wrong with this sign?

# Historical Character

## Difficulty Rating ☆☆☆☆

# HOROBOD

What famous character is this?

# Kings and Queens

**Difficulty Rating** ☆☆☆☆

I found an old English coin marked George 1.
How did I know it was a forgery?

# Rays

**Difficulty Rating** ☆☆

Why might you find these in a hospital?

# Riddle Ruse

Difficulty Rating ☆☆☆

**St. Ives**
**5km**

This is an old riddle.

As I was going to St. Ives
I met a man with seven wives.
Each wife had seven sacks,
Each sack had seven cats,
Every cat had seven kittens;
Kittens, cats, sacks, wives.

How many were going to St. Ives?

# Cosmic Crash

## Difficulty Rating ★★★★

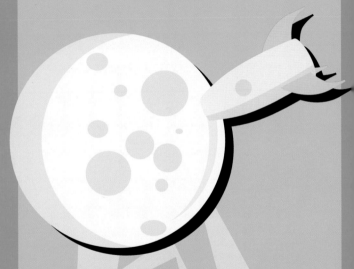

The spacecraft, Seeker 2, crashed into a hostile planet.
The whole surface was solid rock.
Where did they bury the survivors?

# Work It Out

### Difficulty Rating ★★★

$$1 \times 9 \times 5 \times 4 \times 6 \times 7 \times 2 \times 0 = ?$$

What's the answer to this sum?

# Ship Ahoy!

## Difficulty Rating ☆☆☆☆☆

The rungs of the ladder on the side of the ship are
1 foot apart and 8 rungs are showing.
The tide raises the water level by 4 feet.
How many rungs will be covered by the water?

# Word Scramble

## Difficulty Rating ☆

# NOW LO YONDER

Rearrange these words to make one word only.

# Arm Stretch

### Difficulty Rating ☆☆☆☆☆

How can two people each stand on the end
of a piece of string 25cm long, and yet not be able
to touch each other?

# Money Money Money

## Difficulty Rating ☆☆

What is the difference between a crisp new $10 bill and a dirty old torn one?

# Subtraction Mayhem

Difficulty Rating ☆

How many times can you subtract 6 from 36?

# Financial Ruin

### Difficulty Rating ☆☆☆

A woman stopped her car opposite a row of hotels
and immediately knew she was bankrupt. How?

# Definition Derby

What can be made, bent, laid down,
and broken but never touched?

# Place Names

Difficulty Rating ☆

# Calgary

# Detroit

What will you find in the center of Calgary,
that you cannot find in Detroit?

# Wooded Tale

## Difficulty Rating ☆☆☆

Sam walked halfway into the woods in 20 minutes.
Jane claimed that she had gone two-thirds of the way
into the woods in the same amount of time,
but Sam knew this was impossible. Why?

# Soaking Wet

### Difficulty Rating ☆☆

Four friends were walking back home together after leaving the restaurant. It started to rain so they began to run. Three of them got soaking wet hair, but one of them didn't, even though he was not wearing a hat or carrying an umbrella; neither did he stop to take shelter. How could this be?

# Strong Man

## Difficulty Rating ☆☆

Jim Holdup has held the title of Strongest Man in the World for 3 consecutive years yet there is one thing – that weighs virtually nothing – that he finds impossible to hold for more than a couple of minutes. What is it?

# Clean Up

## Difficulty Rating ☆

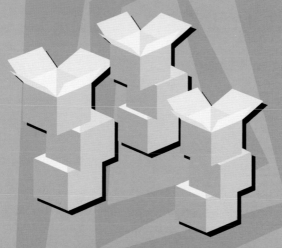

The shop assistants were clearing the shop shelves of empty boxes. Each assistant made a pile by the shelf he was cleaning, until there were 9 piles by one shelf, 7 by the second and 5 by the third. The trainee assistant was then ordered to gather each pile and put them all together at one end of the shop.
How many piles will he have when he is finished?

# Bungalow View

Difficulty Rating ☆☆☆☆

A boy lives in a bungalow where all the windows
in all of the rooms on each side of the house face
in the same direction.
Which are the two possible places that he could live?

# Escaped Prisoner

### Difficulty Rating ☆☆☆

A new prison has been built in the middle of a vast lake. One morning, it's discovered that a prisoner who can't swim has escaped. The only evidence he leaves behind is a strand of shoelace. How did he do it?

# Clowning Around

### Difficulty Rating ☆☆

The clown stuck a pin in a balloon
without popping it. How?

# Birthday Present

## Difficulty Rating ★★

Carl's dad gave him a 28-day watch for his birthday.
How long will it go without winding?

# Fire Fire!

### Difficulty Rating ☆

Pam's new school was a modern, 4-storey building.
On her first day the school caught fire.
Without hesitating, Pam jumped straight out of the
nearest window – yet she was unhurt.
How could this be?

# Ball Challenge

**Difficulty Rating ☆☆☆**

How can you throw a ball as hard as you can in one direction and yet have it come directly back to you?

# That's Magic

## Difficulty Rating ☆☆☆☆☆

Peter the Pirate has caught Felicity the Fairy and put
her into a bottle with the cork in to stop her escaping.
Can you help Dashing Dan get her out, but without
taking out the cork or breaking the glass?

# Nineteen

**Difficulty Rating** ☆

How can you make the following sum add up to 19?

# Strange Object

## Difficulty Rating ☆☆☆☆

Out for a hike and pushing through some thick prickly bushes, Beth put her hand in her pocket and found something with no legs and lots of teeth. What was it?

# Sweet Success

## Difficulty Rating ☆☆☆☆

John works in a candy shop. He has brown hair and is 1.8 meters tall. He has blue eyes. What does he weigh?

# Judo Japes

### Difficulty Rating ⭐⭐

Two judo experts take a bow and the match begins.
One is wearing a brown belt and the other a black belt.
After a long tussle, the black belt judo player has the
most points and is declared the winner, despite the
fact that throughout the entire contest no man threw
the other to the ground. Explain.

# Time's Up

### Difficulty Rating ☆☆☆

Which of these timekeepers has the most moving parts?

# Family Disaster

Difficulty Rating ☆☆☆☆

A father and son were both in a house that caught fire.
The son jumped from a high window and was badly
injured. He was rushed to hospital. As he was wheeled
into the operating theater, the surgeon cried out,
"Oh no! That's my son!" How can that be?

# Tight Fit

## Difficulty Rating ☆☆

A bus attempted to drive under a low bridge but got
stuck underneath it. People tried to help the driver
push the vehicle, but they couldn't free it.
How did they eventually do it?

# 10th Floor Visit

## Difficulty Rating ☆☆☆☆☆

Alice regularly visits her grandfather on the tenth floor of an apartment building. She travels in the elevator to the 9th floor, then walks up a flight of stairs to the 10th floor. Last year she only took the elevator to the 7th floor and walked up three flights of stairs. Why?

Why?

# Twins

**Difficulty Rating** ☆☆☆☆☆

Two brothers have newborn babies exactly 10 hours old.
One baby was born in the evening, the other at midday.
How can that be?

# Clue Words

## Difficulty Rating ☆

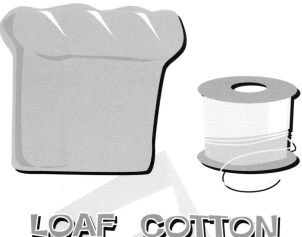

# LOAF   COTTON

Can you find two words that mean the same as the clue words, but which rhyme with each other?

# Odd One Out

ICU

ICAB

ICM

ICAP

Which row of letters is the odd one out?

# Apple Share

## Difficulty Rating ☆☆☆☆

Can you share out the apples so that four friends
each get an apple, but one remains on the plate?

# Road Rage

## Difficulty Rating ☆☆☆☆☆

Bob has just bought a new car. On his way home from work, he is so excited at the prospect of showing it to his girlfriend that he is not concentrating. He goes past a red light without stopping, bumps into someone in front of him and then turns into a 'No Entry' road.
A police officer observes his actions but makes no attempt to arrest him. Why?

# What Am I?

Difficulty Rating ☆☆

Use these clues to work out what the object is:
## Wood, ivory, keys, notes.

# To and Fro

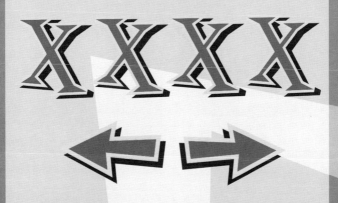

What four-letter word reads the same forwards,
backwards and upside down?

# Mike the Mechanic

## Difficulty Rating ☆☆☆☆

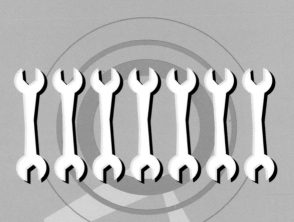

Can you help Mike the Mechanic rearrange these
7 spanners to form 6 triangles?

# 2 Words

**Difficulty Rating** ☆

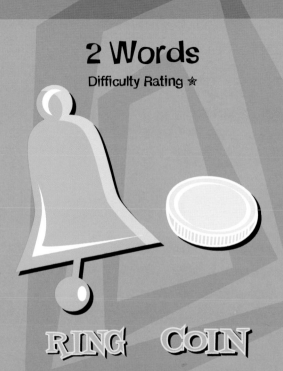

## RING  COIN

Can you find two words that mean the same as the clue words, but which rhyme with each other?

# Triple Teaser

Difficulty Rating ☆☆☆

Three pupils are each asked to select four numbers
under ten and multiply them together.
They all come up with the same answer,
even though they don't all pick the same numbers. How?

# A Hole Lot of Earth

How much earth is there in a hole
290cm wide, 210cm deep and 380cm long?

# Figure It Out

### Difficulty Rating ★★★

$$3+1+8=349$$

Can you add one straight line to this sum
to make it correct?

# A Strange Find

## Difficulty Rating ☆☆

You are walking along in a field in early Spring
and find two lumps of coal and a carrot.
How did they get there?

# Ouch!

Difficulty Rating ☆☆

A man walked into a bar and immediately fell
unconscious. Why?

# Clued-Up

Difficulty Rating ✩✩✩

Use the clues to work out what the object in the box is:
## Drink, pot, bean

# It's the Playing
# that Counts

## Difficulty Rating ⭐⭐

What can be played and lost but never won?

# Rhyming Riddle

## Difficulty Rating ★★★★

SHOW

HIDE

Can you find two words that mean the same as the clue words, but which rhyme with each other?

# Strike a Light

### Difficulty Rating ✮✮✮

What would happen if you struck a match in a
room filled with hydrogen?

# Lunch Time

Difficulty Rating ★★★★

ASEP

SETORCEWN

QAHSUS

TOTPAO

If someone gave you this, what would you be eating?

# Insomnia

## Difficulty Rating ⭐⭐⭐

A woman is awake night after night without getting
a wink of sleep, yet she doesn't feel tired. Why?

# Survivor

Difficulty Rating ☆☆☆

A prisoner survived ten weeks in a cell without water and with a 20cm thick steel door between him and a fresh water well in the next cell. How?

# Coat Conundrum

## Difficulty Rating ☆

What kind of coat contains no buttons,
no arms, no stitching, no cloth,
no pockets and is always put on wet?

# Cat Caper

## Difficulty Rating ☆☆

A man drives to the bank, gets out of his car, closes
and locks all the doors and windows and leaves his car
completely empty. When he returns 5 minutes later
a cat is sitting in the passenger seat looking up at him.
How did the cat get in the car?

# Shopping Bag

## Difficulty Rating ★★★★

I bought 9 apples, which I carried home in 4 bags,
each bag containing an odd number of apples.
How is that possible?

# Big Mouth

## Difficulty Rating ⭐⭐

What has a big mouth, which is forever open,
yet cannot utter one word?

# Two Numbers

## Difficulty Rating ☆☆☆☆

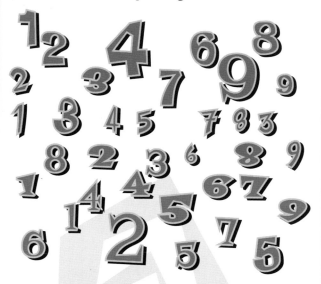

Can you arrange any two numbers side by side so that the number on the right is twice as large, but the number on the left is twice as many?

# No Panic

## Difficulty Rating ☆☆

A trainee pilot was circling the airfield in a light aircraft
and suddenly ran out of fuel; however, he didn't panic,
because he knew he was in no danger.
Why is that?

# All the Twos

### Difficulty Rating ☆☆☆

Take away 2 from 222.
How many different answers can you come up with?

# Missing Letter

### Difficulty Rating ★★★

The same letter is missing five times from this series of letters. What letter is missing?

# Jumping Horse

## Difficulty Rating ☆☆

A horse jumps over a tower and the tower disappears.
.It's not an illusion or a dream so where
could this happen?

# Pick Up

## Difficulty Rating ☆☆

A taxi driver went to pick up two Canadian visitors
arriving at Los Angeles airport. Because he had never
met either of them and did not know what they looked
like he held up a piece of card with their names on.
When the visitors saw the card and came over
to him he immediately said to one of them,
"You must be Philip". How did he know?

# Bonus Question

Difficulty Rating ★★★★

The quiz master asked the contestant,
"Can you name a famous event that happened on
31 September 1985?" "No, I cannot", said the
contestant. "That's correct", said the quiz master.
Why was the answer correct?

# Play Time

**Difficulty Rating** ★★★★

While playing a game with some friends I said,
"If we all put both our hands on the table, how many
hands is that on the table?". "Obviously it is six in total",
said Sally. "No", said Jake, "it is nine".
Why was Jake correct?

# Transport

Difficulty Rating ☆☆

What form of transport has 8 wheels but carries only one passenger?

# Bed Time

### Difficulty Rating ☆☆☆

I knocked on my brother's bedroom door and asked
him a question to which he replied "yes".
I knew he was lying. What was the question?

# Winning Streak

## Difficulty Rating ☆☆☆☆

I won three races at my school sports day,
yet I did not once pass the finishing line.
How was that possible?

# Painters
# and Decorators

### Difficulty Rating ☆☆

Why are so many artists Dutch?

# Monkey Capers

## Difficulty Rating ☆☆☆☆☆

A monkey had been walking all day and was thirsty. He came to a hole with water at the bottom, too far down for him to reach. Beside the hole was a pile of stones. How did the monkey reach the water?

# Window Wonder

Difficulty Rating ☆☆

Fred was cleaning the windows of the eighteenth floor
of an office block when there was a massive power
failure. The electric hoist on his platform was
immobilized, so how did he manage to get down
before the power was restored?

# Solutions

**Page 6 - Shopping Bags**
Mrs Simpson.
Three bags filled with shopping are heavier than four empty bags.

**Page 7 - Summer Holiday**
The letter Y.

**Page 8 - Tea Time**
The man left his house just before the clocks were set back for daylight saving in the Fall. His wife set the clock to show the correct time.

**Page 9 - Spoken Word**
Silence.

**Page 10 - Light Source**
The man was a lighthouse keeper. By turning off all the lights he had turned off the beacon light at the top of the lighthouse. Unable to see the rocky shore, a ship had run aground and six sailors had to swim to safety.

**Page 11 - Common Touch**
They all have a mouth.

**Page 12 - One Giant Leap**
The woman was doing a bungee jump.

**Page 13 - Bailing Out**
Neither hit the ground.
The plane was over the sea!

**Page 14 - Magic Circle**
It's Middle Earth – the setting for the Lord of the Rings.

**Page 15 - Newspaper Round**
Charlie is Mr Hopkins' dog.

**Page 16 - Word Play**
There are no letter 'e's.

**Page 17 - Wrong Sign**
If you can't read, you won't be able to read this notice either.

**Page 18 - Historical Character**
Robin Hood.
<Rob 'in' Hood>.

**Page 19 - Kings and Queens**
No coin would be marked George I. At the time this king was alive it would not be known that there would be a George II, therefore, the coin would simply be marked George.

**Page 20 - Rays**
They are X-rays.

**Page 21 - Riddle Ruse**
One, just me. The others were coming towards me, <u>from</u> St. Ives.

**Page 22 - Cosmic Crash**
The survivors would not need burying because they were alive.

**Page 23 - Work It Out**
0.
Anything multiplied by 0 = 0!

**Page 24 - Ship ahoy!**
None, as the ship, together with the ladder, rises with the tide.

**Page 25 - Word Scramble**
The letters can be arranged to spell ONE WORD ONLY.

**Page 26 - Arm Stretch**
Thread the string under a closed door.

**Page 27 - Money Money Money**
$9.
The difference between a $10 and a $1.

**Page 28 - Subtraction Mayhem**
Once.
After that you are taking it away from 30, then 24, then 18, etc, etc.

**Page 29 - Financial Ruin**
She was playing a game of Monopoly.

**Page 30 - Definition Derby**
Rules.

**Page 31 - Place Names**
The letter 'g'.

**Page 32 - Wooded Tale**
You can only walk halfway <u>into</u> the wood. After that you're walking <u>out</u> of the wood.

**Page 33 - Soaking Wet**
He did not get wet hair because he was bald.

**Page 34 - Strong Man**
His breath.

**Page 35 - Clean Up**
If he puts them all together, he will have one pile.

**Page 36 - Bungalow View**
Either on the North Pole where all the windows face south or on the South Pole where all the windows face north.

**Page 37 - Escaped Prisoner**
The escape happened in winter when the lake had frozen over. He had skated his way to freedom on ice skates, one of which had a broken shoelace.

**Page 38 - Clowning Around**
The balloon wasn't blown up.

**Page 39 - Birthday Present**
It won't go at all without winding.

**Page 40 - Fire Fire!**
Pam was on the ground floor.

**Page 41 - Ball Challenge**
Throw it up in the air.

**Page 42 - That's Magic**
Push the cork into the bottle, then shake the fairy out.

**Page 43 - Nineteen**
Turn the page upside down.

**Page 44 - Strange Object**
Her comb!

**Page 45 - Sweet Success**
He weighs candy!

**Page 46 - Judo Japes**
The two judo players were women.

**Page 47 - Time's Up**
The egg timer – it is filled with thousands of grains of sand.

**Page 48 - Family Disaster**
The surgeon was the boy's mother.

**Page 49 - Tight Fit**
They let some air out of the tyres and then pushed the bus free.

**Page 50 - 10th Floor Visit**
Alice is a child and can only reach the 9th floor button. Last year she was smaller and could only reach the 7th floor button.

**Page 51 - Twins**
One brother lives in Singapore and his baby was born at 8pm. The other baby was born at midday on a winter's day in England, which is 8 hours behind.

**Page 52 - Clue Words**
Bread and thread.

**Page 53 - Odd One Out**
ICM.
The others make sense when spoken.

**Page 54 - Apple Share**
Take 3 apples from the plate and hand one each to three of the friends. Give the fourth friend the plate with the last apple on it.

**Page 55 - Road Rage**
Bob was walking home. His new car had been delivered to his house.

**Page 56 - What am I?**
Piano.

**Page 57 - To and Fro**
NOON.

**Page 58 - Mike the Mechanic**

**Page 59 - 2 Words**
Chime. Dime.

**Page 60 - Triple Teaser**
They all selected 0 as one of their four numbers, so all their totals were 0.

### Page 61 - A Hole Lot of Earth
None.
It's a hole!

### Page 62 - Figure It Out

Add an extra stroke to the first plus sign to turn it into a 4.

### Page 63 - A Strange Find
Some children built a snowman there. It is now warm and the snow has melted leaving only the coal and the carrot, which had been the snowman's eyes and nose.

### Page 64 - Ouch!
It was an iron bar.

### Page 65 - Clued-Up
Coffee.

### Page 66 - It's the Playing that Counts
A musical instrument.

### Page 67 - Rhyming Riddle
Reveal and conceal.

### Page 68 - Strike a Light
Nothing.
The match could not burn if there was no oxygen in the room.

### Page 69 - Lunch Time
Mixed vegetables.
Peas, sweetcorn, squash and potato.

### Page 70 - Insomnia
She is a nurse and works the night shift at her local hospital. She sleeps during the day.

### Page 71 - Survivor
The steel door wasn't locked.

### Page 72 - Coat Conundrum
A coat of paint.

### Page 73 - Cat Caper
It was a convertible car and the top was down. The cat simply jumped in through the open top.

### Page 74 - Shopping Bag
I had 3 apples each in three bags and then put the three bags into a larger bag which, therefore, contained 9 apples.

**Page 75 - Big Mouth**
A river.

**Page 76 - Two Numbers**
6$3$ or 4$2$ or 8$4$, etc.

**Page 77 - No Panic**
He hadn't yet taken off.

**Page 78 - All the Twos**
There are two answers, the obvious one of 222 – 2 = 220 but there is another one, 222 less one of the 2s is 22!

**Page 79 - Missing Letter**
S.
SEVEN LESS SIX IS ONE.

**Page 80 - Jumping Horse**
In a game of chess.

**Page 81 - Pick Up**
The other visitor was a lady.

**Page 82 - Bonus Question**
September has only 30 days.
31 September does not exist.

**Page 83 - Play Time**
The game we were playing was cards. The other 3 hands were the three hands of cards that had already been dealt.

**Page 84 - Transport**
A pair of roller skates.

**Page 85 - Bed Time**
"Are you asleep?"

**Page 86 - Winning Streak**
They were swimming races. In swimming the winner is the first to touch the finishing line at the end of the pool, but he does not pass it.

**Page 87 - Painters and Decorators**
Because they were born in Holland.

**Page 88 - Monkey Capers**
He dropped the stones into the water until the water rose high enough for him to drink.

**Page 89 - Window Wonder**
Fred walked down the stairs. He was cleaning the windows from the inside.